THE MONKEY'S PAW

You can make three wishes. You can ask for three things – anything in the world. You can wish for the moon, the sun, the stars. How wonderful, you say. But think about it for a minute. When your wish comes true, that is only the beginning. When you change one thing, then you change another, and another. Perhaps you don't want these other changes, but how can you stop them?

The White family in this story can make three wishes. At first they laugh, and say, 'It's not possible. And what can we wish for? What do we need?' But they make a wish, and then they wait for something to happen.

The next day, their first wish comes true, and suddenly, their life is like a terrible, terrible dream . . .

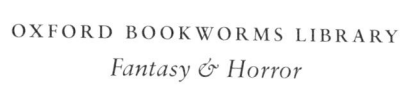

OXFORD BOOKWORMS LIBRARY
Fantasy & Horror

The Monkey's Paw

Stage 1 (400 headwords)

Series Editor: Jennifer Bassett
Founder Editor: Tricia Hedge
Activities Editors: Jennifer Bassett and Alison Baxter

W. W. JACOBS

The Monkey's Paw

Retold by
Diane Mowat

OXFORD UNIVERSITY PRESS

OXFORD

UNIVERSITY PRESS

Great Clarendon Street, Oxford OX2 6DP

Oxford University Press is a department of the University of Oxford.
It furthers the University's objective of excellence in research, scholarship,
and education by publishing worldwide in

Oxford New York

Auckland Cape Town Dar es Salaam Hong Kong Karachi
Kuala Lumpur Madrid Melbourne Mexico City Nairobi
New Delhi Shanghai Taipei Toronto

With offices in

Argentina Austria Brazil Chile Czech Republic France Greece
Guatemala Hungary Italy Japan Poland Portugal Singapore
South Korea Switzerland Thailand Turkey Ukraine Vietnam

OXFORD and OXFORD ENGLISH are registered trade marks of
Oxford University Press in the UK and in certain other countries

ISBN 978 0 19 478910 3

A complete recording of this Bookworms edition of
The Monkey's Paw is available.

Printed in China

Illustrated by: Kevin Jones

The publishers are grateful to the Society of Authors,
as literary repesentatives of the Estate of W.W. Jacobs,
for permission to create this simplified edition

Word count (main text): 4830 words

For more information on the Oxford Bookworms Library,
visit www.oup.com/elt/bookworms

CONTENTS

Chapter 1

It was cold and dark out in the road and the rain did not stop for a minute. But in the little living-room of number 12 Castle Road it was nice and warm. Old Mr White and his son, Herbert, played chess and Mrs White sat and watched them. The old woman was happy because her husband and her son were good friends and they liked to be together. 'Herbert's a good son,' she thought. 'We waited a long time for him and I was nearly forty when he was born, but we are a happy family.' And old Mrs White smiled.

It was true. Herbert was young and he laughed a lot, but his mother and his father laughed with him. They had not got much money, but they were a very happy little family.

The two men did not talk because they played carefully. The room was quiet, but the noise of the rain was worse now and they could hear it on the windows. Suddenly old Mr White looked up. 'Listen to the rain!' he said.

'Yes, it's a bad night,' Herbert answered. 'It's not a good night to be out. But is your friend, Tom Morris, coming tonight?'

Old Mr White and his son played chess.

'Yes, that's right. He's coming at about seven o'clock,' the old man said. 'But perhaps this rain . . .'

Mr White did not finish because just then the young man heard a noise.

'Listen!' Herbert said. 'There's someone at the door now.'

'I didn't hear a noise,' his father answered, but he got up from his chair and went to open the front door. Mrs White got up too and began to put things away.

Mr White said, 'Come in, come in, Tom. It's wonderful to see you again. What a bad night! Give me your coat and then come into the living-room. It's nice and warm in there.'

The front door was open, and in the living-room Mrs White and Herbert felt the cold. Then Mr White came back into the living-room with a big, red-faced man.

'This is Tom Morris,' Mr White told his wife and son. 'We were friends when we were young. We worked together before Tom went to India. Tom, this is my wife and this is our son, Herbert.'

'Pleased to meet you,' Tom Morris said.

'Pleased to meet you, Mr Morris,' Mrs White answered. 'Please come and sit down.'

'Yes, come on, Tom,' Mr White said. 'Over here. It's nice and warm.'

'Thank you,' the big man answered and he sat down.

'Let's have some whisky,' old Mr White said. 'You need something to warm you on a cold night.' He got out a bottle of whisky and the two old friends began to drink and talk. The little family listened with interest to this visitor from far away and he told them many strange stories.

Chapter 2

After some time Tom Morris stopped talking and Mr White said to his wife and son, 'Tom was a soldier in India for twenty-one years. India is a wonderful country.'

'Yes,' Herbert said. 'I'd like to go there.'

'Oh, Herbert!' his mother cried. She was afraid because she did not want to lose her son.

'I wanted to go to India too,' her husband said, 'but . . .'

'It's better for you here!' the soldier said quickly.

'But you saw a lot of strange and wonderful things in India. I want to see them too one day,' Mr White said.

The soldier put down his whisky. 'No!' he cried. 'Stay here!'

Old Mr White did not stop. 'But your stories were

4

'Let's have some whisky,' old Mr White said.

interesting,' he said to Tom Morris. 'What did you begin to say about a monkey's paw?'

'Nothing!' Morris answered quickly. 'Well . . . nothing important.'

'A monkey's paw?' Mrs White said.

'Come on, Mr Morris! Tell us about it,' Herbert said.

Morris took his whisky in his hand, but suddenly he put it down again. Slowly he put his hand into the pocket of his coat and the White family watched him.

'What is it? What is it?' Mrs White cried.

Morris said nothing. He took his hand out of his pocket. The White family watched carefully – and in the soldier's hand they saw something little and dirty.

Mrs White moved back, afraid, but her son, Herbert, took it and looked at it carefully.

'Well, what is it?' Mr White asked his friend.

'Look at it,' the soldier answered. 'It's a little paw . . . a monkey's paw.'

'A monkey's paw!' Herbert said – and he laughed. 'Why do you carry a monkey's paw in your pocket, Mr Morris?' he asked the old soldier.

'Well, you see,' Morris said, 'this monkey's paw is magic!'

Herbert laughed again, but the soldier said, 'Don't laugh, boy. Remember, you're young. I'm old now and

Herbert looked carefully at the monkey's paw.

'An old Indian gave the monkey's paw to one of my friends.'

in India I saw many strange things.' He stopped talking for a minute and then he said, 'This monkey's paw can do strange and wonderful things. An old Indian gave the paw to one of my friends. My friend was a soldier too. This paw is magic because it can give three wishes to three people.'

'Wonderful!' Herbert said.

'But these three wishes don't bring happiness,' the soldier said. 'The old Indian wanted to teach us something – it's never good to want to change things.'

'Well, did your friend have three wishes?' Herbert asked the old soldier.

'Yes,' Morris answered quietly. 'And his third and last wish was to die!'

Mr and Mrs White listened to the story and they felt afraid, but Herbert asked, 'And did he die?'

'Yes, he did,' Morris said. 'He had no family, so his things came to me when he died. The monkey's paw was with his things, but he told me about it before he died,' Tom Morris finished quietly.

'What were his first two wishes, then?' Herbert asked. 'What did he ask for?'

'I don't know. He didn't want to tell me,' the soldier answered.

For a minute or two everybody was quiet, but then

Herbert said, 'And you, Mr Morris: did you have three wishes?'

'Yes, I did,' Morris answered. 'I was young. I wanted many things – a fast car, money . . .' Morris stopped for a minute and then he said with difficulty, 'My wife and my young son died in an accident in the car. Without them I didn't want the money, so, in the end, I wished to lose it. But it was too late. My wife and my child were dead.'

The room was very quiet. The White family looked at the unhappy face of the old soldier.

Then Mr White said, 'Why do you want the paw now? You don't need it. You can give it to someone.'

'How can I give it to someone?' the soldier said. 'The monkey's paw brings unhappiness with it.'

'Well, give it to me,' Mr White said. 'Perhaps this time it . . .'

'No!' Tom Morris cried. 'You're my friend. I can't give it to you.' Then, after a minute, he said, 'I can't give it to you, but, of course you can take it from me. But remember – this monkey's paw brings unhappiness!'

Old Mr White did not listen and he did not think. Quickly, he put out his hand, and he took the paw.

Tom Morris looked unhappy, but Mr White did not want to wait.

'What do I do now?' he asked his friend.

'The monkey's paw brings unhappiness with it.'

'What can I wish for? We need money, of course.'

'Yes, come on, Father,' Herbert said. 'Make a wish!' And he laughed.

The soldier said nothing and Mr White asked him again, 'What do I do now?'

At first the old soldier did not answer, but in the end he said quietly, 'OK. But remember! Be careful! Think before you make your wish.'

'Yes, yes,' Mr White said.

'Take the paw in your right hand and then make your wish, but . . .' Tom Morris began.

'Yes, we know,' Herbert said. 'Be careful!'

Just then old Mrs White stood up and she began to get the dinner. Her husband looked at her. Then he smiled and said to her, 'Come on. Help me! What can I wish for? We need money, of course.'

Mrs White laughed, but she thought for a minute and then she said, 'Well, I'm getting old now and sometimes it's difficult to do everything. Perhaps I need four hands and not two. Yes, ask the paw to give me two more hands.'

'OK, then,' her husband said, and he took the monkey's paw in his right hand. Everybody watched him and for a minute he waited. Then he opened his mouth to make his wish.

Suddenly Tom Morris stood up. 'Don't do it!' he cried.

The old soldier's face was white. Herbert and his mother laughed, but Mr White looked at Tom's face.

Old Mr White was afraid and he put the monkey's paw into his pocket.

After a minute or two they sat down at the table and began to have dinner. The soldier told the family many strange and wonderful stories about India. They forgot the monkey's paw, and because the soldier's stories were interesting, they asked him many questions about India. When Tom Morris stood up to leave, it was very late.

'Thank you for a very nice evening,' Morris said to the family. 'And thank you for a very good dinner,' he said to Mrs White.

'It was a wonderful evening for us, Tom,' old Mr White answered. 'Your stories were very interesting. Our life isn't very exciting and we don't have the money to visit India, so please come again soon. You can tell us some more stories about India.'

Then the old soldier put on his coat. He said goodbye to the White family, and went out into the rain.

The soldier told the family many stories about India.

Chapter 3

It was nearly midnight. In their warm living-room, the two old people and their son sat and talked about the soldier's stories.

'India is a wonderful country,' Mr White said. 'What exciting stories! It was a good evening.'

Mrs White stood up to take some things into the kitchen, but she stopped and listened to Herbert and his father.

'Yes,' Herbert said. 'Morris told some interesting stories, but, of course, some of them weren't true.'

'Oh Herbert!' Mrs White said.

'Well, Mother, that story about the monkey's paw wasn't true. A dirty little monkey's paw isn't magic! But it was a good story.' And Herbert smiled.

'Well, I think you're right, Herbert,' his mother said.

'I don't know,' Mr White said quietly. 'Perhaps the story was true. Strange things can happen sometimes.'

Mrs White looked at her husband. 'Did you give some money to Tom Morris for that paw?' she asked. 'We don't have money to give away for nothing!' Mrs White was angry now.

'Well, yes,' her husband answered. 'I did, but not

'Perhaps the story was true.'

much, and at first he didn't want to take it. He wanted the monkey's paw.'

'Well, he can't have it,' Herbert laughed. 'It's our paw now and we're going to be rich and happy. Come on, Father. Make a wish!'

Old Mr White took the paw from his pocket. 'OK, Herbert, but what am I going to ask for? I have everything – you, your mother. What do I need?'

'Money, of course,' Herbert answered quickly. 'We need money! You're always thinking about money. That's because we haven't got very much of it. With money you can pay for this house. It can be your house! Go on, Father, wish for thirty thousand pounds!'

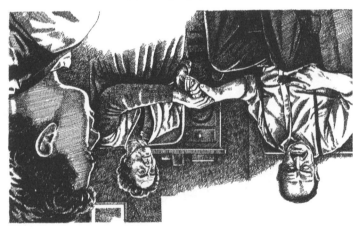

'I wish for £30,000.'

Herbert stopped talking and his old father thought for a minute. The room was quiet and they could hear the rain on the windows.

Then Mr White took the monkey's paw in his right hand. He was afraid, but he looked at his wife and she smiled at him.

'Go on,' she said.

Slowly and carefully Mr White said, 'I wish for thirty thousand pounds.'

Suddenly he gave a cry and Mrs White and Herbert ran to him.

'What's the matter, Father?' Herbert asked.

'It moved!' Mr White cried. 'The monkey's paw – it moved!'

They looked at the paw. It was now on the floor and not in the old man's hand. The family watched it, and they waited – but it did not move again.

So the little family sat down again and they waited. Nothing happened. The noise of the rain on the windows was worse now and their little living-room did not feel nice and warm.

Mrs White said, 'It's cold. Let's go to bed.'

Mr White did not answer and in the end Herbert said, 'Well, there's no money, Father. Your friend's story wasn't true.' But Mr White did not answer. He sat quietly and said nothing.

After some time Mrs White said to her husband, 'Are you OK?'

'Yes, yes,' the old man answered, 'but for a minute or two I was afraid.'

'Well, we needed that money,' Mrs White said, 'but we aren't going to get it. I'm tired. I'm going to bed.'

After Mrs White went to bed, the two men sat and smoked for some time.

Then Herbert said, 'Well, Father, I'm going to bed too. Perhaps the money is in a bag under your bed! Goodnight, Father.' And Herbert laughed and went out of the room.

Old Mr White sat in the cold living-room for a long time. The candle died and it was dark. Suddenly, the old

Suddenly, he saw a face at the window.

man saw a face at the window. Quickly, he looked again, but there was nothing there. He felt afraid. Slowly he stood up and left the cold, dark room.

Chapter 4

The next morning the winter sun came through the window and the house felt nice and warm again. Mr White felt better and he smiled at his wife and son. The family sat down to have breakfast and they began to talk about the day. The monkey's paw was on a little

'I'm going to work,' Herbert said.

table near the window, but nobody looked at it and nobody thought about it.

'I'm going to the shops this morning,' Mrs White said. 'I want to get something nice for dinner. Are you going to come with me?' she asked her husband.

'No, I'm going to have a quiet morning. I'm going to read,' her husband answered.

'Well, I'm not going to go out this evening,' Herbert said, 'so we can go to bed early tonight. We were very late last night.'

'And we aren't going to have stories about monkeys' paws!' Mrs White said. She was angry. 'Why did we listen to your friend?' she asked her husband. 'A monkey's paw can't give you things!' She stopped but the two men did not answer her. 'Thirty thousand pounds!' she said quietly. 'We needed that money.'

Just then Herbert looked at the clock and stood up. 'I'm going to work,' he said. 'Perhaps the postman has got the money for you in a letter. Remember, I want some of it too!' Herbert laughed and his mother laughed too.

'Don't laugh, son,' Mr White said. 'Tom Morris is an old friend and he thinks the story is true. Perhaps it is.'

'Well, leave some of the money for me,' Herbert laughed again.

His mother laughed too and she went to the door with him.

'Goodbye, Mother,' Herbert said happily. 'Get something nice for dinner this evening at the shops. I'm always hungry after a day at work.'

'I know you are!' Mrs White answered.

Herbert left the house and walked quickly down the road. His mother stood at the door for some time and watched him. The winter sun was warm, but suddenly she felt very cold.

Mrs White stood at the door for some time.

Chapter 5

Slowly, old Mrs White went back into the house. Her husband looked up and saw something strange in her face.

'What's the matter?' he asked.

'Nothing,' his wife answered, and she sat down to finish her breakfast. She began to think about Tom Morris again and suddenly she said to her husband, 'Your friend drank a lot of whisky last night! A monkey's paw! What a story!'

Mr White did not answer her because just then the postman arrived. He brought two letters for them – but there was no money in them. After breakfast the two old people forgot about the money and the monkey's paw.

Later in the day, at about one o'clock, Mr and Mrs White sat down to eat and then they began to talk about money again. They did not have very much money, so they often needed to talk about it.

'That thirty thousand pounds,' Mrs White said, 'we need it!'

'But it didn't come this morning,' her husband answered. 'Let's forget it!'

Then he said, 'But that thing moved. The monkey's paw moved in my hand! Tom's story was true?'

'You drank a lot of whisky last night. Perhaps the paw didn't move,' Mrs White answered.

'It moved?' Mr White cried angrily.

At first his wife did not answer, but then she said, 'Well,' Herbert laughed about it . . .'

Suddenly she stopped talking. She stood up and went over to the window.

'What's the matter?' her husband asked.

'There's a man in front of our house,' Mrs White answered. 'He's a stranger – very tall – and well dressed.

'There's a tall, well-dressed stranger in front of our house.'

'Can I come in and talk to you?'

He's looking at our house . . . Oh, no . . . it's OK . . . He's going away . . .'

'Come and sit down! Finish eating!' Mr White said.

The old woman did not listen to her husband. 'He isn't going away,' she went on. 'He's coming back. I don't know him – he's a stranger. Yes, he's very well dressed . . .' Suddenly Mrs White stopped. She was very excited. 'He's coming to the door . . . Perhaps he's bringing the money!'

And she ran out of the room to open the front door.

The tall, well-dressed stranger stood there. For a minute he said nothing, but then he began, 'Good afternoon. I'm looking for Mr and Mrs White.'

'Well, I'm Mrs White,' the old woman answered. 'What can I do for you?'

At first the stranger did not answer, but then he said, 'Mrs White, I'm from Maw and Meggins. Can I come in and talk to you?'

Maw and Meggins had a big factory and Herbert White worked there on the machinery.

'Yes, of course,' Mrs White answered. 'Please come in.'

The well-dressed stranger came into the little living-room and Mr White stood up.

'Are you Mr White?' the stranger began. Then he went on, 'I'm from Maw and Meggins.'

Mrs White looked at the stranger and she thought, 'Perhaps he has the money . . . but why Maw and Meggins? And his face is very unhappy . . . Why?' Suddenly the old woman was afraid.

'Please sit down,' Mr White began, but now his wife could not wait.

'What's the matter?' she cried. 'Is Herbert . . .' She could not finish the question.

The stranger did not look at their faces – and Mr White began to be afraid too.

'Please, tell us!' he said.

'I'm very sorry,' the man from Maw and Meggins began. He stopped for a minute and then he began again. 'I'm very sorry, but this morning there was an accident at the factory . . .'

'What's the matter? Is Herbert OK?' Mrs White cried again.

'Well . . .' the man began slowly.

'Is he in hospital?' the old woman asked, very afraid now.

'Yes, but . . .' the stranger looked at Mrs White's face and stopped.

'Is he dead? Is Herbert dead?' Mr White asked quietly.

'Dead!' Mrs White cried. 'Oh no . . . please . . . not dead! Not Herbert! Not our son!'

'This morning there was an accident at the factory . . .'

Suddenly the old woman stopped because she saw the stranger's face. Then the two old people knew. Their son was dead! Old Mrs White began to cry quietly and Mr White put his arm round her.

Some time later the man from Maw and Meggins said, 'It was the machinery – an accident. Herbert called, "Help!". The men heard him – and ran to him quickly, but they could do nothing. The next minute he was in the machinery. I'm very, very sorry,' he finished.

For a minute or two the room was quiet. At last Mrs White said, 'Our son! Dead! We're never going to see him again. What are we going to do without him?'

Her husband said, 'He was our son. We loved him.'

'Maw and Meggins want to help you at this unhappy time.'

Then Mrs White asked the stranger, 'Can we see him? Can we see our son? Please take me to him. I want to see my son.'

But the stranger answered quickly, 'No!' he said. 'It's better not to see him. They couldn't stop the machinery quickly. He was in there for a long time. And at first they couldn't get him out. He was . . . ?' The man stopped.

Then he said, 'Don't go to see him.'

The stranger went over to the window because he did not want to see the faces of the two old people. He said nothing, but he stood there for some time and he waited.

Then he went back to the old people and began to

30

talk again. 'There's one more thing,' he said. 'Your son worked for Maw and Meggins for six years and he was a good worker. Now Maw and Meggins want to help you at this unhappy time.' Again the stranger stopped. After a minute he began again. 'Maw and Meggins want to give you some money.' Then he put something into Mr White's hand.

Old Mr White did not look at the money in his hand. Slowly he stood up and looked at the stranger, afraid. 'How much?' Mr White asked, very quietly. He did not want to hear the answer.

'Thirty thousand pounds,' the stranger said.

Chapter 6

Three days later, in the big, new cemetery two miles from their house, the two old people said goodbye to their dead son. Then they went back to their dark, old house. They did not want to live without Herbert, but they waited for something good to happen, something to help them. The days went by very slowly. Sometimes they did not talk because there was nothing to say without Herbert. And so the days felt very long.

Then, one night, about a week later, Mrs White got out of bed because she could not sleep. She sat by the

The two old people said goodbye to their dead son.

window and she watched and waited for her son. He did not come and she began to cry quietly.

In the dark her husband heard her and he called, 'Come back to bed. It's cold out there.'

'It's colder for my son,' his wife answered. 'He's out there in the cold cemetery.'

Mrs White did not go back to bed, but Mr White was old and tired and the bed was warm. So, in the end, he went to sleep again. Suddenly he heard a cry from his wife.

'The paw!' she cried. 'The monkey's paw!' She came back to the bed and stood there.

'What is it? What's the matter?' Mr White cried. He sat up in bed. 'What's the matter?' he thought. 'Why is she excited? What's she talking about?' He looked at his wife.

Her face was very white in the dark. 'I want it,' she said quietly, 'and you've got it! Give it to me! Please!'

'What?' Mr White asked.

'The monkey's paw,' Mrs White said. 'Where is it?'

'It's downstairs,' Mr White answered. 'Why?'

Mrs White began to laugh and cry. 'We can have two more wishes!' she cried. 'We had one – but there are two more!'

'Oh, no! Not again! Think, woman!' Mr White cried. But Mrs White did not listen.

'The monkey's paw! We can have two more wishes!'

'Quickly,' she said. 'Go and get the paw. We're going to wish for our boy to come back to us!'

'No!' Mr White cried. 'You're mad!'

'Get it! Get it quickly!' Mrs White cried again.

Mr White said again, 'Think, woman! Think! Our boy was in the machinery for a long time. They didn't want to show him to us! Think! Do you want to see his body?'

'Yes! He's my son. I'm not afraid of him!' she answered.

'You don't understand,' Mr White said sadly, but he went downstairs to look for the monkey's paw.

In the living-room it was dark and Mr White did not have a candle. Slowly, he went across the room and he

'I wish for my son, Herbert, to come back to us.'

put out his hand for the monkey's paw. He touched it, and quickly took his hand away again.

'No?' he thought. 'I can't! I don't want to see Herbert! His face – after he was in the machinery . . . no!'

Then he thought about his wife – and he put out his hand and took the paw.

In the bedroom his wife waited. She saw the paw in Mr White's hand and cried, 'Quick! Make the wish!'

'I can't,' Mr White answered. 'Remember – he died in the machinery!'

'Make the wish! I'm not afraid of my own son!' Mrs White cried again.

Mr White looked sadly at his wife, but he took the

paw in his right hand and said slowly, 'I wish for my son, Herbert, to come back to us.' Then he sat down in the nearest chair.

But Mrs White went over to the window and looked out into the road. She stayed there for a long time and she did not move. Nothing happened. The monkey's paw could not do it!

'Thank God!' Mr White said, and he went back to bed.

Soon Mrs White went to bed too.

Chapter 7

But they did not sleep. They waited and they listened. In the end Mr White got up to get a candle because the dark made him more afraid. He began to go downstairs, but suddenly he heard a noise at the front door. He stopped, and he listened. He could not move. Then the noise came again. This time he ran. He ran upstairs, back into the bedroom and he closed the door behind him. But again the noise came.

'What's that?' Mrs White cried, and she sat up in bed.

'Nothing! Go to sleep again!' her husband answered.

But Mrs White listened – and the noise came again.

'The paw!' Mr White thought. 'Where's the monkey's paw?'

'It's Herbert! It's Herbert!' she cried. 'I'm going to open the door for him.'

And she got out of bed and ran to the door of the bedroom. Mr White got there first and stopped her.

'No!' he cried. 'Think!'

'But it's my boy! It's Herbert,' she answered.

'No! Don't go! Don't . . .' her husband cried again.

But Mrs White did not listen to him. She opened the bedroom door and ran from the room. 'I'm coming, Herbert. I'm coming!' she called.

Mr White ran after her. 'Stop!' he cried. 'Remember, Herbert died in the machinery! You don't want to see him!'

For a minute Mrs White stopped and looked at her husband, but then the noise came again and she began to run downstairs.

'Help me! Help me!' she called to her husband.

But Mr White did not move. 'The paw!' he thought. 'Where's the monkey's paw?'

He ran back into the bedroom. 'Quick!' he thought. 'Where is it?' At first he could not find it in the dark. Ah! There it was! He had it!

Just at that minute he heard his wife downstairs.

'Wait! Wait, Herbert! I'm coming!' she cried. She began to open the front door.

At the same time Mr White took the monkey's paw in

The road was dark and quiet.

his right hand and he made his third wish.

Mrs White gave a long unhappy cry and her husband ran down to her. She stood by the open door. Very afraid, old Mr White looked out into the dark.

The road was dark and quiet – and there was nobody there.

GLOSSARY

candle a stick of wax that burns to give light

cemetery a place where we put dead people in the ground

chess a game; two people play it with chess pieces (chessmen) on a black and white board

factory a big building where workers make things

go on not stop; continue

happiness being happy

idea a plan or new thought (when you think of something new)

Indian *(n)* a person from India

kitchen the room where you cook food

living-room the room where you sit and talk

machinery machines which make things in a factory

mad ill in the head

magic something which can do strange and wonderful things

monkey a small animal with a long tail; it lives in trees in hot countries

paw the hand or foot of an animal

pay to give money to get something

put away to put things in their usual places

sad not happy

show to let someone see something

soldier a man who fights for his country

strange different, unusual; that you do not know or understand

terrible very, very bad

Thank God! when something bad does not happen, we say this to show we are thankful

together with somebody or something
touch to put your hand or finger on something
unhappy not happy
whisky a strong drink from Scotland
wish *(v)* to want something that is not usually possible
wish *(n)* something that you want very much; **make a wish** to ask for something that can only happen by magic

The Monkey's Paw

ACTIVITIES

Before Reading

1 **Read the introduction on the first page of the book, and the back cover. How much do you know now about the story? Tick one box for each sentence.**

	YES	NO
1 The White family is waiting for a visitor.	☐	☐
2 The visitor is a young woman.	☐	☐
3 The visitor comes from Africa.	☐	☐
4 The visitor brings the family a cat's foot.	☐	☐
5 The White family can make three wishes.	☐	☐
6 After the family's first wish comes true, something terrible happens.	☐	☐

2 **What was the family's first wish? Can you guess? Choose one of these wishes.**

1 To be happy.

2 To have an expensive car and a new house.

3 To have a lot of money.

4 To be famous.

5 To live a very long time.

6 To go round the world on a ship.

Imagine that you can have a wish too. What do *you* wish for?

ACTIVITIES

───────────

While Reading

Read Chapters 1 and 2. Choose the best question-word, and then answer these questions.

What / Who

1 . . . lived at number 12 Castle Road?
2 . . . were friends when they were young?
3 . . . was a soldier in India for many years?
4 . . . was strange about the monkey's paw?
5 . . . gave the monkey's paw to Tom Morris's friend?
6 . . . was his friend's third wish?
7 . . . did Tom Morris wish for?
8 . . . died in a car accident?
9 . . . took the monkey's paw from Tom Morris?
10 . . . did Mrs White want to wish for first?

Read Chapters 3 and 4. Here are some untrue sentences about them. Change them into true sentences.

1 Herbert wanted his father to wish for happiness.
2 Mr White wished for a million pounds.
3 When Mr White wished, the monkey's paw spoke.
4 Later, Mr White saw a face on the living-room wall.
5 Herbert did not laugh about the money.
6 The next morning Herbert went out to play football.

45

Before you read Chapter 5, can you guess what happens?

1 How does the thirty thousand pounds come?
2 Is the family happy when the money comes?

Read Chapter 5, and then answer these questions.

1 Who did Mrs White see in front of the house?
2 Why was she excited?
3 Where was the stranger from?
4 Where did Herbert work?
5 What happened at the factory that morning?
6 What did Mrs White want to do?
7 Who said, 'Don't go to see him!', and why did he say it?
8 What did the stranger give to Mr White?

Read Chapter 6. How many true sentences can you make from this table?

		excited and could not sleep.
	was	afraid of the monkey's paw.
Mr White	wanted	to make a second wish.
Mrs White	thought	to see Herbert again.
	didn't want	about Herbert in the machinery.
	didn't think	happy when nobody came.
		unhappy when nobody came.

46

Before you read Chapter 7, can you guess what happens? Choose one of these answers.

1 Herbert does not come back to 12 Castle Road.
2 Herbert comes back to 12 Castle Road, alive and well.
3 Herbert comes back, but he is dead.
4 Herbert comes back, and Mr White makes a third wish.

Read Chapter 7, then match these halves of sentences.

1 When Mr White went downstairs to get a candle, . . .
2 He ran quickly back upstairs into the bedroom . . .
3 But Mrs White heard the noise too, and wanted to go to the front door . . .
4 Mr White tried to stop her, . . .
5 She called to her husband to help her, . . .
6 When his wife began to open the front door, . . .
7 Then he went downstairs and the two old people looked out into the dark, . . .
8 because she thought it was Herbert.
9 Mr White took the monkey's paw in his hand and made his third wish.
10 and closed the door behind him.
11 but Mr White ran back into the bedroom.
12 but there was nobody there.
13 he heard a noise at the front door.
14 but she did not listen to him, and she ran downstairs.

After Reading

1 What was Mr White's last wish? Choose one of these answers.

1 For his son to come into the house.

2 For his wife to see nobody at the door.

3 For his son to go back to the cemetery and stay there.

4 For the noise at the door to be just a dog or a cat.

5 For his son to die a second time.

2 Perhaps Tom Morris's friend wrote a letter to Tom before he died. Complete his letter with these linking words.

before / after / and / and / because / so / but / but

Dear Tom,

I am going to die soon _____ I want you to read this letter _____ I am dead. I have no family, _____ you can have all my things. You can have the monkey's paw too, _____ be very careful. Think _____ you make a wish. My life was very unhappy _____ I wished for the wrong things. It's never good to want to change things, _____ the wishes don't bring happiness. The old Indian told me that, _____ I did not listen to him. So, please be careful, Tom.

3 **Find words from the story to complete these sentences. Then fit the words into the puzzle below.**

1 Tom Morris told many _____ and wonderful stories.

2 The monkey's paw was _____.

3 Tom Morris took the monkey's paw out of his _____.

4 The monkey's paw could give three _____ to three people.

5 An old _____ gave the paw to Tom Morris's friend.

6 Herbert worked in a _____.

7 Tom Morris was a _____ in India.

8 The wishes bring _____.

9 Mr White's first wish was for _____.

10 Herbert's dead body was in the _____.

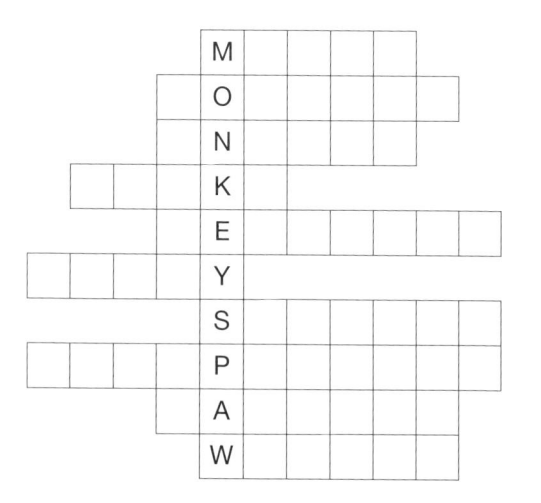

4 **A year later Tom Morris comes back to see Mr White. Write out their conversation in the correct order and put in the speakers' names. Mr White speaks first (number 3).**

1 _____ 'I'm very sorry, my friend. Very, very sorry. I lost my son, too. How did the money come to you?'

2 _____ 'That's true. But why did you talk about it?'

3 _____ 'I don't want to talk to you, Tom Morris. Your monkey's paw brought unhappiness to this house.'

4 _____ 'And I was the third person, and I made three wishes. So, is the magic finished now?'

5 _____ 'What do you mean, "it was the paw"?'

6 _____ 'Why are you unhappy? What did you wish for?'

7 _____ 'The factory gave us thirty thousand pounds because of the accident. But we didn't want the money – we wanted our son! Oh, why did you give me that monkey's paw?'

8 _____ 'Yes, thank God. The story of the monkey's paw is finished.'

9 _____ 'I mean, I couldn't stop the magic. The paw wanted to go from me to you. It had work to do – to give three wishes to three people.'

10 _____ 'I didn't give it to you. You took it from me.'

11 _____ 'I wished for thirty thousand pounds – and the next day our son Herbert died in an accident.'

12 _____ 'I didn't want to talk about it – it was the paw.'

5 **Choose a good (G) title for each chapter. One title is not good (NG). Explain why.**

Chapter 1

A game of chess / The visitor from India / A happy family

Chapter 2

The magic paw / A car accident / Four hands

Chapter 3

The first wish / Stories from India / The face at the window

Chapter 4

A quiet morning / Herbert goes to work / Mrs White is afraid

Chapter 5

The money comes / Goodbye, Herbert / Two old people

Chapter 6

Waiting for Herbert / A cold night / The second wish

Chapter 7

A noise at the door / The third wish / The cemetery

6 **Think about the story, and then answer these questions.**

1 You have three wishes. What do you ask for?

2 Somebody gives you the monkey's paw. What do you do with it?

3 'It's never good to want to change things.' Do you agree with that?

ABOUT THE AUTHOR

William Wymark Jacobs was born in the East End of London in 1863. He worked for the Civil Service, and in the 1890s he began to write stories for magazines such as *The Idler* and *Strand Magazine*. His first book of short stories, *Many Cargoes*, came out in 1896. This was very successful, and Jacobs left his office job because he wanted more time for writing. He wrote a number of novels – *At Sunwich Port* (1902) and *Dialstone Lane* (1904), for example – but we remember him today because of his short stories. His best book of stories was probably *Light Freights* (1901). He died in 1943.

Jacobs wrote two kinds of short story. Some of them were funny stories, about sailors and people who lived in small villages. The other kind were horror stories, like *The Monkey's Paw*. This first came out in a magazine in 1902, and was later made into a successful play for the theatre. It is his most famous story, and appears in collections of horror stories again and again. In the story we never see the terrible face of the Whites' dead son at the front door, but we can feel the horror of it, waiting in the dark.

OXFORD BOOKWORMS LIBRARY

Classics • Crime & Mystery • Factfiles • Fantasy & Horror
Human Interest • Playscripts • Thriller & Adventure
True Stories • World Stories

The OXFORD BOOKWORMS LIBRARY provides enjoyable reading in English, with a wide range of classic and modern fiction, non-fiction, and plays. It includes original and adapted texts in seven carefully graded language stages, which take learners from beginner to advanced level. An overview is given on the next pages.

All Stage 1 titles are available as audio recordings, as well as over eighty other titles from Starter to Stage 6. All Starters and many titles at Stages 1 to 4 are specially recommended for younger learners. Every Bookworm is illustrated, and Starters and Factfiles have full-colour illustrations.

The OXFORD BOOKWORMS LIBRARY also offers extensive support. Each book contains an introduction to the story, notes about the author, a glossary, and activities. Additional resources include tests and worksheets, and answers for these and for the activities in the books. There is advice on running a class library, using audio recordings, and the many ways of using Oxford Bookworms in reading programmes. Resource materials are available on the website <www.oup.com/bookworms>.

The *Oxford Bookworms Collection* is a series for advanced learners. It consists of volumes of short stories by well-known authors, both classic and modern. Texts are not abridged or adapted in any way, but carefully selected to be accessible to the advanced student.

You can find details and a full list of titles in the *Oxford Bookworms Library Catalogue* and *Oxford English Language Teaching Catalogues*, and on the website <www.oup.com/bookworms>.

THE OXFORD BOOKWORMS LIBRARY
GRADING AND SAMPLE EXTRACTS

STARTER • 250 HEADWORDS

present simple – present continuous – imperative –
can/cannot, must – *going to* (future) – simple gerunds ...

Her phone is ringing – but where is it?

Sally gets out of bed and looks in her bag. No phone. She looks under the bed. No phone. Then she looks behind the door. There is her phone. Sally picks up her phone and answers it. *Sally's Phone*

STAGE 1 • 400 HEADWORDS

... past simple – coordination with *and, but, or* –
subordination with *before, after, when, because, so* ...

I knew him in Persia. He was a famous builder and I worked with him there. For a time I was his friend, but not for long. When he came to Paris, I came after him – I wanted to watch him. He was a very clever, very dangerous man. *The Phantom of the Opera*

STAGE 2 • 700 HEADWORDS

... present perfect – *will* (future) – *(don't) have to, must not, could* –
comparison of adjectives – simple *if* clauses – past continuous –
tag questions – *ask/tell* + infinitive ...

While I was writing these words in my diary, I decided what to do. I must try to escape. I shall try to get down the wall outside. The window is high above the ground, but I have to try. I shall take some of the gold with me – if I escape, perhaps it will be helpful later. *Dracula*

STAGE 3 • 1000 HEADWORDS

... should, may – present perfect continuous – *used to* – past perfect –
causative – relative clauses – indirect statements ...

Of course, it was most important that no one should see
Colin, Mary, or Dickon entering the secret garden. So Colin
gave orders to the gardeners that they must all keep away
from that part of the garden in future. *The Secret Garden*

STAGE 4 • 1400 HEADWORDS

... past perfect continuous – passive (simple forms) –
would conditional clauses – indirect questions –
relatives with *where/when* – gerunds after prepositions/phrases ...

I was glad. Now Hyde could not show his face to the world
again. If he did, every honest man in London would be
proud to report him to the police. *Dr Jekyll and Mr Hyde*

STAGE 5 • 1800 HEADWORDS

... future continuous – future perfect –
passive (modals, continuous forms) –
would have conditional clauses – modals + perfect infinitive ...

If he had spoken Estella's name, I would have hit him. I was
so angry with him, and so depressed about my future, that I
could not eat the breakfast. Instead I went straight to the old
house. *Great Expectations*

STAGE 6 • 2500 HEADWORDS

... passive (infinitives, gerunds) – advanced modal meanings –
clauses of concession, condition

When I stepped up to the piano, I was confident. It was as if I
knew that the prodigy side of me really did exist. And when
I started to play, I was so caught up in how lovely I looked
that I didn't worry how I would sound. *The Joy Luck Club*

Sister Love and Other Crime Stories

JOHN ESCOTT

Some sisters are good friends, some are not. Sometimes there is more hate in a family than there is love. Karin is beautiful and has lots of men friends, but she can be very unkind to her sister Marcia. Perhaps when they were small, there was love between them, but that was a long time ago.

They say that everybody has one crime in them. Perhaps they only take an umbrella that does not belong to them. Perhaps they steal from a shop, perhaps they get angry and hit someone, perhaps they kill . . .

Ned Kelly: A True Story

CHRISTINE LINDOP

When he was a boy, he was poor and hungry. When he was a young man, he was still poor and still hungry. He learnt how to steal horses, he learnt how to fight, he learnt how to live outside the law. Australia in the 1870s was a hard, wild place. Rich people had land, poor people didn't. So the rich got richer, and the poor stayed poor.

Some say Ned Kelly was a bad man. Some say he was a good man but the law was bad. This is the true story of Australia's most famous outlaw.